Marco M

He's a joker w
messing abou
always means
if he sometim
things wrong.

Waxy Max

He's very sporty and
football mad. On the
outside, he's tough,
but underneath he's
got the biggest heart.

Philippa Feltpen

A real peacemaker, she
helps keep the other
Pens in order by sorting
out arguments and giving
good advice.

Don't worry,
Splodge. We'll
stick together.

Squiggle and Splodge

The Scribble twins! They're
both quiet, both shy. Although
they may not look alike, they
do almost everything together.

Enter ...

Squiggle, how much do you love me?

Lots! Probably more than sweets!

Pens

Helping you to get to know God more

God's Love

Written by

Alexa Tewkesbury

Every day a short Bible reading is brought to life with the help of the Pens characters. A related question and prayer apply this to daily life. Written in four sections, two focusing on the lives of Pens and two on Bible characters, young children will be inspired to learn more of God and His Word.

What's inside?

CWR

FSC
www.fsc.org

MIX
Paper from responsible sources
FSC® C016973

LOVING EACH OTHER

'… if I have no love, I am nothing.' (1 Corinthians 13 v 2)

Someone new

There was someone new in Pens' town.

He didn't look like Pens. He wasn't very friendly either.

Um … hello.

4

'Humph!' huffed the Someone New.

'What's your name?' asked Marco.

'Harumph!' puffed the Someone New.

'Are you just visiting?' asked Charlotte.

'Why is it,' grumbled the Someone New, 'that I can't go on holiday without being asked questions?' And he shuffled away.

'How rude,' frowned Gloria.

'Very rude indeed,' agreed Denzil.

'Perhaps he's just shy,' suggested Philippa. 'Let's try to make friends again next time we see him.'

 God wants us to be kind to people, even if they don't seem very friendly.

Do you like making new friends?

Pens Prayer

Dear Lord God, I want to be loving and kind always – just like You. Amen.

5

Day 2 — Loving Each Other

'… love your enemies and pray for those who persecute you …' (Matthew 5 v 44)

marco's invitation

There was someone new in Pens' town. Marco saw him in the park.

Hello. I'm going skateboarding. Would you like to have a go?

The Someone New didn't answer.

'After that,' continued Marco, 'Denzil and I are going swimming. You can come with us if you like.'

'I don't like swimming,' scowled the Someone New, 'and I don't know how to skateboard.' And he slipped away.

'I'm not sure I like that Someone New,' muttered Marco.

'Let's pray for him,' said Charlotte. 'We can ask God to help him make friends.'

When someone is unfriendly, we can show love by praying for them.

Is there anyone you'd like God to help this week? Tell Him about them now.

Pens Prayer

Heavenly Father, please help me remember to pray for people who need Your love. Amen.

Day 3

Loving Each Other

'... love does not keep a record of wrongs ...'
(1 Corinthians 13 v 5)

The wrong flowers

8

There was someone new in Pens' town. He'd spotted some flowers by Gloria's gate. He loved the taste of flowers – so he munched and he chomped until they were all gone.

Gloria came outside.

'Where did I leave my hat?' she wondered.

Then she saw it … lying by her gate.

'Nooo!' she screeched.

The flowers the Someone New had eaten were the flowers on Gloria's hat!

'What's wrong?' frowned Denzil.

'Look what the Someone New has done!' shouted Gloria.

'Oh dear,' said Denzil. 'Try not to be cross. Perhaps he didn't realise he was eating your hat.'

 We can show God's love to someone who has upset us by forgiving them.

The Someone New loves the taste of flowers. What do you love the taste of?

Pens Prayer

Father God, teach me to forgive other people, just as You always forgive me. Amen.

Day 4 — Loving Each Other

'Love your enemies and do good to them ...' (Luke 6 v 35)

'Go away!'

There was someone new in Pens' town. He was watching Max and Sharpy playing football.

Max kicked the ball. It landed right next to the Someone New.

Puffing and panting, Sharpy chased after it.

Suddenly –

'Go away!' yelled the Someone New. 'I don't like dogs!'

Sharpy stopped running and his ears drooped down.

'It's all right, Sharpy,' said Max quietly. 'Let's get the ball and go home.'

When Max told Charlotte, she smiled, 'I think you did the right thing. If you'd been cross, there might have been an argument. God's much happier when we don't get angry.'

 If anyone talks to us crossly, God always hopes that we won't speak crossly back to them.

Why do you think Sharpy's ears 'drooped down'?

Pens Prayer

Father God, please help me not to cause arguments, but to love other people the way You love them. Amen.

'Why should God reward you if you love only the people who love you?' (Matthew 5 v 46)

making friends

There was someone new in Pens' town, and Squiggle and Splodge couldn't stop thinking about him.

I remember when *we* were new here. It was lonely until we started making friends.

'That's what we should do,' smiled Squiggle. 'Even if the Someone New's not staying in Pens' town for long, we should help him make friends.'

So Squiggle and Splodge decided to hold a 'making friends' party. They invited all Pens, and when everything was organised they asked the Someone New.

'Please come to our party,' they said, 'because Pens can't wait to make friends with you.'

 If someone seems lonely, God wants us to show them love by being a friend.

Is there anyone new at your school or preschool who you could make friends with?

Pens Prayer

Please help me, dear Lord, always to be ready to be a friend. Amen.

'Love is patient and kind …' (1 Corinthians 13 v 4)

The grumblers

There was someone new in Pens' town, and Squiggle and Splodge were very cross with him.

We organised a whole party.

14

'A WHOLE PARTY!' moaned Splodge. 'But the Someone New we organised the WHOLE PARTY for didn't bother to come.'

'If I ever see him again,' snapped Squiggle, 'I'm not even going to speak to him.'

Philippa looked thoughtful.

'Please don't be grumblers,' she said. 'The Someone New should have told you he wasn't coming to the party, but it would make God sad if you stopped trying to be his friends.'

 Showing God's love means being patient and ready to forgive other people.

Do you find it easy or hard to be patient?

Pens Prayer

I praise You, Lord God, that Your love for me is always patient and forgiving. Thank You. Amen.

Loving Each Other

'… if you do good only to those who do good to you, why should you receive a blessing?' (Luke 6 v 33)

A flying football

There was someone new in Pens' town. He was sleeping under a tree.

He slept right through lunch time and he stayed asleep until –

THUMP! – a football thudded into him.

'I'm SO sorry!' called Max, running over. 'I didn't mean to hit you.'

Max waited for the Someone New to get cross.

But the Someone New didn't.

Instead, he looked puzzled.

'Why are you so kind to me?' he asked. 'After all, I haven't been kind to you.'

Max shrugged. 'It's because of Jesus,' he said. 'People weren't always kind to Him, but He never stopped being kind to them.'

 Jesus teaches us how to show God's love to other people.

If you do something wrong, why is it important to say sorry?

Pens Prayer

Dear Lord, I thank You so much that Your HUGE love for me is the same every single day. Amen.

Day 8

Loving Each Other

'... love is not ill-mannered or selfish or irritable ...'
(1 Corinthians 13 v 5)

On the beach

18

There was someone new in Pens' town. He was down at the beach. Pens were having a barbecue and the food looked delicious.

'Shall we invite the Someone New to share our barbecue?' asked Charlotte.

'Why?' replied Squiggle. 'We invited him to our party and he didn't come.'

'*And* he ate my hat,' added Gloria. 'He really is very rude.'

'It's not kind to leave someone out, though,' said Philippa. 'That would make us rude, too. If we're going to show love the way God wants us to, we can't be selfish. I'll go and invite him now.'

However we feel about someone, God wants us to show His love by being kind and thoughtful.

How do you think it feels to be 'left out'?

Pens Prayer

Lord God, please help me remember how much EVERYONE needs Your love. Amen.

19

Day 9 — Loving Each Other

'Love never gives up …' (1 Corinthians 13 v 7)

Denzil makes a friend

There was someone new in Pens' town. He was gazing up at the moon in the night sky.

'Hello,' Denzil smiled, slipping outside to see him. 'Aren't you sleepy?'

'Not tonight,' answered the Someone New. 'So I thought I'd enjoy a spot of moonlight.'

'I'll keep you company,' Denzil said.

'Wouldn't you rather be in bed?' asked the Someone New.

'That's all right,' Denzil replied. 'If *I* couldn't sleep, I'd like it if someone sat up with me.'

'Thank you …' said the Someone New. '… And my name's Sticky.'

 God never stops loving us – and He never wants us to stop loving others.

What different ways can you think of to be loving and kind?

Pens Prayer

My Father God, I want to shine with Your love so that other people will see You in me. Amen.

21

'Love the Lord your God with all your heart, with all your soul, with all your mind, and with all your strength.' (Mark 12 v 30)

Goodbye time

Sorry you're not sticking around

Made by Pens

There was someone new in Pens' town, but it was the end of his holiday. Sticky was going home.

Pens decided to give him a special goodbye card, and Gloria made him a goodbye hat.

'You can think of us every time you wear it,' she beamed.

'You're all SO kind,' mumbled Sticky, 'even though I've been SO grumpy.'

'If we've been kind,' Marco said cheerfully, 'it's because that's how God wants us to be. We try to love God more than anything else – and when you love someone that much, you just want to make them happy.'

When we love God, we need to love and care for other people, too.

Who makes you happy? Say thank you to God for them now.

Pens Prayer

Thank You, dear God, for being my best Friend. Please teach me to love You more every day. Amen.

HANNAH'S PROMISE
For the love of God

Day 11

'… Hannah … cried bitterly as she prayed to the Lord.' (1 Samuel 1 vv 9–10)

Hannah wants a baby

Hannah wanted a baby. More than anything else in the whole world. A baby of her very own.

Every year, she and her husband went away to stay at a special place called Shiloh. Lots of people met there to pray and to worship God.

But one year at Shiloh Hannah was so miserable she didn't even feel like eating.

'All around me there are children,' she sobbed. 'But I have none. I want a baby more than anything else in the whole world.'

 Hannah worshipped God even though she was so unhappy.

Do you tell God when you feel unhappy?

Pens Prayer

Thank You, dear Lord, that I can talk to You when I feel sad, because You love to listen. Amen.

Hannah's Promise
For the love of God

Day 12

'If you give me a son, I promise that I will dedicate him to you for his whole life ...' (1 Samuel 1 v 11)

Hannah's prayer

Hannah began to pray. As she talked to God, tears rolled down her cheeks.

'Please hear me, Lord,' she cried. 'Don't forget about me! I'm *so* sad. I want a baby of my own. A little child to love and care for. If You will only give me a son, I promise to bring him here to Shiloh when he is old enough so that he can work for You.'

Eli, the priest who served God at Shiloh, saw how upset Hannah was.

'God bless you,' he said, 'and I pray that He'll give you what you've asked for.'

Hannah cried out to God and made Him a special promise.

Do you think God heard Hannah's prayer?

Pens Prayer

My Father God, I praise You that You never grow tired of listening to my prayers. Amen.

Hannah's Promise
For the love of God

Day 13

'Then [Hannah] went away, ate some food, and was no longer sad.' (1 Samuel 1 v 18)

much better

When Hannah had finished talking to God, she began to feel better. She even felt hungry again and had something to eat.

'You look happier,' smiled her husband.

'That's because I am,' nodded Hannah.

Hannah had been able to tell God about everything that was making her sad. Now she was calmer because she was sure He had listened to her. She knew God loved her, and she could trust Him to do what was best.

Talking to God about being sad helped Hannah feel better.

Do you ever talk to God when you are on your own?

Pens Prayer

Lord God, if something makes me sad, please help me remember that You love me and want to share my problems. Amen.

Hannah's Promise
For the love of God

Day 14

'... the LORD answered [Hannah's] prayer.'
(1 Samuel 1 v 19)

A most wonderful thing

The day after Hannah had talked to God about a baby, it was time to leave Shiloh. So she and her husband packed up and set off for home.

But they hadn't been back long when it happened – the most wonderful thing!

God answered Hannah's prayer.

'Yes,' He said. 'You will have a baby of your own. A little child to love and care for.'

'Oh, thank You, Lord!' Hannah cried. 'You've made me SO happy!'

When Hannah's son was born, she kissed him and she cuddled him.

And she gave him the name Samuel.

 Hannah praised God because He had answered her prayer.

Do you know someone who has a new baby?

Pens Prayer

Dear God, sometimes You answer yes and sometimes You answer no. But thank You that I can trust You always. Amen.

Hannah's Promise
For the love of God

Day 15

'As long as he lives, he will belong to the LORD.'
(1 Samuel 1 v 28)

Hannah keeps her promise

Hannah loved her Samuel.

But she loved God, too. She couldn't forget the promise she had made to Him.

'Samuel,' she said, 'you are God's wonderful present to me. Now you are old enough, I must take you to Shiloh to work for Him there.'

When they arrived, Eli the priest said kindly, 'I'll look after you, Samuel. We'll work for God together.'

Hannah was very sad to leave Samuel, but she visited him every year.

And because she'd kept her promise to God, He gave her more children – brothers and sisters for her very first baby.

By keeping her promise, Hannah showed God how much she loved Him.

What can you do to show God that you love Him?

Pens Prayer

Heavenly Father, thank You for giving Your love to me. I want to give my love to You, too. Amen.

BLESSINGS FROM GOD

'Happy are those who know they are spiritually poor; the Kingdom of heaven belongs to them!' (Matthew 5 v 3)

A coat and a warm hat, of course.

'I'm *so* hungry,' said Splodge. 'Guess what I need?'

Squiggle replied, 'Something to eat, of course.'

'I'm *so* bored,' said Max. 'Guess what I need?'

Charlotte replied, 'Something to do, of course.'

'I *so* want a best friend,' said Denzil. 'Someone who's kind and patient, loving and forgiving. Guess who I need?'

Philippa replied, 'Our Father God. When you tell God you need Him, He'll help you with everything else you need. And He'll always give you His love.'

 God loves us to need Him. Then He can be our very best Friend.

Marco needs a coat and a hat because he's cold. How else can you warm yourself up?

Pens Prayer

Dear Lord God, thank You for being my best Friend. I need Your love every day. Amen.

35

Max was feeling sad.

'It can be so hard doing what God wants you to do,' he mumbled. 'Sometimes I get annoyed with Sharpy. Or I get cross when I can't find my football. Or I don't feel like sharing my things. God can't be very pleased with me.'

'That's silly!' smiled Philippa. 'God knows we find it hard always doing the right thing. We just have to keep trying. But as soon as we say sorry to Him for the wrong things we do, that's when He can forgive us and help us feel happy again.'

God is always ready to comfort us when we're sad, and to forgive us when we say sorry.

If one of your friends is sad, how can you comfort them?

Pens Prayer

Dear Father, I'm sorry for the wrong things I sometimes do. Thank You so much for forgiving me. Amen.

37

Blessings from God

'Happy are those who are humble; they will receive what God has promised!' (Matthew 5 v 5)

Denzil in hospital

When Denzil was in hospital because he'd broken his arm, Charlotte had a cold.

Bother! I've got such a snuffly nose.

But Charlotte's snuffly nose didn't stop her helping Denzil.

She did some tidying and cleaning for him. She did some washing and some ironing.

Charlotte spent all day making things comfortable for when Denzil got home. She even baked some blueberry muffins as a treat for him.

'Thank you so much,' beamed Denzil when he saw everything Charlotte had done. 'You've spent time helping me even though you're not feeling well.'

God will bless us when we give our time happily to help others.

What should you always keep with you when you have a cold?

Pens Prayer

Lord God, I praise You that You are always kind and loving and caring. Teach me to be just like You. Amen.

'Happy are those whose greatest desire is to do what God requires; God will satisfy them fully!' (Matthew 5 v 6)

making
God
happy

Max had a BRILLIANT football. It was black and orange and Marco wanted one just like it.

As Marco walked past the toyshop one day, he heard a THUD. A big basket had fallen over and some coloured balls rolled out through the open doorway.

Something else rolled out, too.

A football – just like Max's.

Marco thought, 'Would anyone notice if I took that home …?'

But Marco didn't take the football home. He gave it to the shopkeeper. Marco knew God would be sad if he'd stolen it – and making God sad would make Marco sad, too.

God will bless us when we live His way. He only wants what's best for us.

What kind of toys do you like playing with?

Pens Prayer

Please teach me, dear Father, to listen to You and to follow You every day. Amen.

41

Day 20 — Blessings from God

'Happy are those who are merciful to others; God will be merciful to them!' (Matthew 5 v 7)

Wet Paint

Philippa had a new garden bench.

I'll paint it blue.

42

She'd just finished when Gloria arrived.

'Just popping in for a chat,' Gloria said.

'Lovely,' smiled Philippa. 'Sit in the garden and I'll bring you some lemonade.'

What Philippa forgot to say was, 'Mind the wet paint …'

When Gloria sat on the wet, blue bench, she looked as if she was going to cry.

'I'm SO sorry,' groaned Philippa.

'Oh …' muttered Gloria crossly. Then –

'Never mind,' she said. 'Accidents happen. I'll go home and get changed.'

God is quick to forgive us when we are quick to forgive other people.

Philippa likes blue. What's your favourite colour?

Pens Prayer

Heavenly Lord, if I upset someone, please help me be quick to say sorry. If someone upsets me, please help me be quick to forgive. Amen.

Blue Paint

43

Day 21 — Blessings from God

'Happy are the pure in heart; they will see God!'
(Matthew 5 v 8)

Swinging

Squiggle and Splodge were swinging – on Marco's gate. Backwards and forwards they went, laughing and giggling.

'I don't think that's a good idea,' frowned Denzil. 'Gates are made for opening and closing – not for swinging on. You'd better get off before it breaks.'

'I'm sure it won't break!' chuckled Squiggle.

'We'll just stay on for a bit longer,' grinned Splodge …

Suddenly –

CRACK! The gate broke and Squiggle and Splodge fell off.

'I did warn you,' said Denzil.

'I know,' mumbled Squiggle. 'I'm sorry.'

'I'm sorry, too,' whimpered Splodge. 'I wish we'd listened to you.'

God loves to bless us when we listen to Him and do as He says.

Do you know how to 'listen' to God?

Pens Prayer

Lord God, please help me to hear Your voice and to do as You teach me. Amen.

Day 22   Blessings from God

'Happy are those who work for peace; God will call them his children!' (Matthew 5 v 9)

Bad dog!

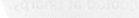

46

'Sharpy!' shouted Charlotte. 'What have you done?'

Sharpy had been playing with the washing on Charlotte's washing line. Towels and pillowcases flapped in the breeze and he'd been trying to catch them.

'Yesss!' he thought as he grabbed a corner of towel in his mouth.

'NOOO!' he thought as the washing line fell down and all the clean washing landed in the mud.

'Bad dog,' groaned Charlotte.

Max hurried over. 'Don't worry, Charlotte,' he said. 'I'll mend the washing line, and I'll wash all your things again.'

Charlotte felt happier.

'Thank you,' she replied. 'Sorry I shouted at Sharpy.'

 God wants to bless us when we comfort and help someone who is upset.

What's the best weather for washing to dry outside?

Pens Prayer

Dear Father, if I see someone who is upset, please help me know the right things to say and the right things to do. Amen.

47

Day 23 — Blessings from God

'Happy are those who are persecuted because they do what God requires; the Kingdom of heaven belongs to them!' (Matthew 5 v 10)

Standing UP for God

Squiggle's and Splodge's faces were unhappy.

Squiggle's and Splodge's eyes were sad.

'What's wrong?' asked Philippa.

'We keep trying to be kind and helpful,' said Squiggle. 'Charlotte says that's what God wants. That's a way to show Him we love Him.'

'And we do love God,' sighed Splodge, 'but sometimes we get teased for trying to do good things.'

'If someone hasn't made friends with God yet,' Philippa explained, 'they may not understand why you want to make Him happy. The most important thing is to keep loving Him. After all, the One who really matters is God.'

God will always bless us when we stand up for Him and do as He says.

How does God want us to behave?

Pens Prayer

Lord God, You are my Father in heaven and I want to follow You always. Amen.

49

Day 24 — Blessings from God

'Remain united to me, and I will remain united to you.'
(John 15 v 4)

Painting Pens

Gloria's house needed a new coat of paint.

I'll do it.

But there was a lot of painting for Denzil to do all on his own.

'I'll help,' said Philippa.

'I'll help, too,' grinned Marco.

'And me,' added Max.

Max needed to climb up a ladder, but he didn't feel safe.

'I'll hold on to it for you,' smiled Charlotte. 'Then you won't have to worry about it falling over.'

'I'll hold on to it with you,' said Gloria. 'We don't want any accidents.'

With so many Pens helping, Gloria's house was looking beautiful in no time.

 God blesses us with His love when we choose to follow Him and care for each other.

How can you stay close to God every day?

Pens Prayer

Dear Father God, thank You so much for being my Friend and my Helper – every single day. Amen.

THE MIRACLE MEAL

Five thousand for supper

Day 25

'So [Jesus] said to them, "Let us go off by ourselves to some place where we will be alone and you can rest for a while."' (Mark 6 v 31)

Jesus needs a rest

Everywhere Jesus went, there were people.

People who wanted to listen to Him teaching about God.

People who were ill and needed Him to make them better.

People who just wanted to be close to Him.

It made Jesus very happy to be able to help them, but He and His disciples often felt tired.

'We need a rest,' Jesus said one day.

So they climbed into a boat and set off to find somewhere quiet.

Jesus loved teaching people about His Father God.

What different types of transport do people use when they go on holiday?

Pens Prayer

Dear Lord, please help me to be ready to tell other people about You – just like Jesus. Amen.

The Miracle Meal
Five thousand for supper

Day 26

'... his heart was filled with pity for them, because they were like sheep without a shepherd.'
(Mark 6 v 34)

Across the lake

'Look over there!' a man shouted. He pointed towards the boat carrying Jesus and His friends. 'If we follow the path quickly round the lake, we should be in time to meet them.'

So the man hurried off with a HUGE crowd of others behind him.

When Jesus and His friends got out of their boat, they could hardly believe their eyes.

'SO many people!' Jesus cried. 'They need me to look after them the way sheep need a shepherd.'

And instead of having a rest, Jesus began to teach them about God's love.

 Jesus is our 'Good Shepherd'.

What kind of animal sometimes helps a farmer with his sheep?

Pens Prayer

Thank You, dear Lord, that as I grow up You are always with me. Amen.

The Miracle Meal
Five thousand for supper

Day 27

'Send the people away ... to buy themselves something to eat.' (Mark 6 v 36)

Hungry tummies

Jesus talked to people all day long. He was so pleased to be teaching them about God that He forgot what time it was. So did the crowds who were listening – until they started to feel hungry.

One of Jesus' friends said to Him, 'You'll have to tell everyone to leave now. They need to go and buy food.'

Jesus just smiled. 'Why don't you find them something to eat?' He replied. 'See if anyone's brought any bread with them.'

Jesus didn't want anyone to go hungry.

Some people say 'grace' before they eat a meal. Do you know what they are doing?

Pens Prayer

Thank You, my Father God, for the food You provide for me. Amen.

The Miracle Meal
Five thousand for supper

Day 28

'There is a boy here who has five loaves of barley bread and two fish.' (John 6 v 9)

one little boy

Jesus' friends began to walk through the crowds of people.

'Has anyone brought any food with them?' they asked.

At last – 'I have,' came a small, timid voice.

It belonged to a little boy. One of Jesus' friends called Andrew smiled at him kindly.

'Well done!' Andrew said. 'What have you got?'

The boy held out his food. There were five bread rolls and two fish.

'Thank you,' said Andrew. 'May I take it to Jesus?'

'Of course,' nodded the boy happily.

 The little boy trusted Jesus and wanted to help Him.

What is your favourite roll or sandwich filling?

Pens Prayer

Lord God, please help me to be like the boy who gave up his food – and to trust in You completely. Amen.

The Miracle Meal
Five thousand for supper

Day 29

'Then Jesus took the five loaves and the two fish, looked up to heaven, and gave thanks to God.' (Mark 6 v 41)

Jesus says thank you

60

When Andrew found Jesus again, he held out the little boy's food.

'There must be about five thousand hungry men here,' he sighed, 'and lots of women and children too. But this is all I could find.'

Jesus looked pleased.

'Thank you,' He beamed. 'That's all I'm going to need. Go and tell everyone to get into groups and sit down.'

The people all made themselves comfy, and Jesus thanked God for the bread and the fish. Then He began breaking them into pieces.

'Now,' He said to His friends, 'you can start handing out a bread and fish supper.'

Jesus knew God would help Him feed the thousands of hungry people.

Who gets your meals ready? Remember to say thank you to them for looking after you.

Pens Prayer

Dear Lord, You care for me in every single way. I really praise You. Amen.

The Miracle Meal
Five thousand for supper

Day 30

'Everyone ate and had enough. Then the disciples took up twelve baskets full of what was left of the bread and the fish.' (Mark 6 vv 42–43)

A super supper

Jesus' friends started to share the food out among the groups of people. But they couldn't help shaking their heads.

'There'll never be enough,' they muttered. 'There are too many people here.'

That's when they began to realise.

The more food they handed out, the more food there seemed to be!

Jesus' friends were astonished. He'd made a miracle meal for thousands of people out of five bread rolls and two fish. Everyone ate until they were full – and when all the leftover pieces were picked up, they filled twelve baskets!

With His miracle meal, Jesus showed people God's power and love.

How do you think the little boy felt when Jesus used his picnic to work a miracle?

Pens Prayer

Thank You so much, dear Father, that You are a God full of love – and surprises! Amen.

Other Pens titles

Friends

Father God

Following Jesus

Really Special

Trusting God

Helping and Serving

Big and Small

God's Book

Available from April 2011.

Pens Special!
Starting School

Help children start school confidently, knowing that God goes there with them. A short story followed by five days of Bible notes.